Programmable
Logic Control
Workbook

City and Guilds Co-publishing Series

City and Guilds of London Institute has a long history of providing assessments and certification to those who have undertaken education and training in a wide variety of technical subjects or occupational areas. Its business is essentially to provide an assurance that pre-determined standards have been met. That activity has grown in importance over the past few years as government and national bodies strive to create the right conditions for the steady growth of a skilled and flexible workforce.

Both teachers and learners need materials to support them as they work towards the attainment of qualifications, and City and Guilds is pleased to be working with several distinguished publishers towards meeting that need. It has been closely involved in planning, author selection and text appraisal, although the opinions expressed in the publications are those of the individual authors and are not necessarily those of the Institute.

City and Guilds is fully committed to the projects listed below and is pleased to commend them to teaching staff, students and their advisers.

Carolyn Andrew and others, *Business Administration Level I* and *Business Administration Level II*, John Murray

David Minton, *Teaching Skills in Further and Adult Education*, Macmillan

Graham Morris and Lesley Reveler, *Retail Certificate Workbook* (Levels 1 and 2), Macmillan

Peter Riley (consultant editor), *Computer-aided Engineering*, and associated Workbooks: *CNC Setting and Operation; CNC Part Programming; Computer-aided Draughting; Robot Technology; Programmable Logic Control*, Macmillan

Barbara Wilson, *Information Technology: the Basics*, Macmillan

Caroline Wilkinson, *Information Technology in the Office*, Macmillan

Programmable Logic Control Workbook

Peter C. Hunt

Department of Construction and Engineering Services
Blackpool and The Fylde College

Consultant Editor: Peter Riley
Formerly Head of Department of Engineering
Technology, Blackpool and The Fylde College

First published 1993 by
THE MACMILLAN PRESS LTD
Houndmills, Basingstoke, Hampshire RG21 2XS
and London
Companies and representatives
throughout the world

ISBN 0–333–56510–X

A catalogue record for this book is
available from the British Library

Printed and bound in Great Britain by
Butler & Tanner Ltd, Frome and London

Contents

Introduction

Programmable logic controllers (PLCs) are essential elements in many industrial processes. The learning assignments in this workbook will provide a broad range of practical experiences which represent a valuable foundation to the successful application of this technology.

The subject is a diverse one, which frequently involves separate elements of a manufacturing process. Because of this, the practical activities have been carefully selected to create a comprehensive yet cohesive programme of study which closely follows the City and Guilds 230 Computer-aided Engineering series Programmable Logic Control syllabus. This workbook will also prove to be a useful aid to those studying standard modules in PLC and process control available through the Business and Technology Education Council (BTEC).

The approach in all the assignments concerns the practical application of PLCs. These range from programming to system monitoring and diagnostics. It is a multi-disciplined technology which demands a multi-skilled engineer for effective application. The workbook will be particularly suitable for:

- recently trained engineers wishing to advance to more specialised new technology work

- mature, skilled and experienced engineers who need to update and enhance their traditional skills with PLC programming and system applications

- service and maintenance personnel who want to broaden their skills and knowledge base in response to multi- and inter-disciplinary developments in PLC technology

- technical trainers and teachers seeking to acquire new technology skills in response to changing course demands.

The result of rapid technological advances in industry is that there has never been a more exciting time to be an engineer. This workbook has been written for those concerned with sharing and exploiting the benefits that may be derived from this new technology and its associated working methods.

City and Guilds/Macmillan publishing for computer-aided engineering

This workbook is one of a series of City and Guilds/Macmillan books which together give complete and up-to-date coverage of computer-aided engineering. A core text, or source book (*Computer-aided Engineering*), gives basic information on all the main topic areas (basic CNC; CNC setting and operation; CNC part programming; CNC advanced part programming; basic CAD/CAM; computer-aided draughting; advanced CAD; basic robotics; robot technology; programmable logic controllers; more advanced programmable logic controllers). It has tasks structured in to the text to encourage active learning.

Workbooks cover five main topics: CNC setting and operation; CNC part programming; computer-aided draughting; robot technology; programmable logic controllers. Each workbook includes all the operational information and guidance needed to be able to complete the practical assignments and tasks.

The books complement each other but can be used independently of each other. Peter Riley (formerly Head of Department of Engineering Technology, Blackpool and The Fylde College) is Consultant Editor of the series.

How to use this book

Each learning assignment in this workbook has a similar structure, to make its use as straightforward as possible. Information and guidance that is needed to be able to complete the practical work is included with each assignment.

You will be able to identify the following parts of the text:

- Background information introducing the topic at the beginning of each assignment.

- Other relevant knowledge given under the heading 'Additional information'.

- In the sections 'Useful observations' you will find points which will help you in becoming familiar with the process and in exploring ways in which it can be used.

- The practical 'Tasks' are presented in a logical sequence so that they can be accomplished safely and successfully. In many cases 'Additional tasks' are included to reinforce and enhance the basic practical work.

- If there is information of particular interest concerning the practical tasks, you will find this under the heading 'A point to note' or 'Points to note'.

All the diagrams and illustrations which are needed for each assignment are given at the appropriate point in the text.

You are recommended to obtain a folder in which to keep work which you have completed. This will serve as a record of your achievements and may be useful for future reference.

General note

Many different programming techniques are used with programmable logic controllers, and it is impossible to refer to all of them in this book.

Where an exercise includes a program, a standard form of ladder diagram has been used. These ladder diagrams are based upon those used with a Toshiba EX20/40 controller, shown in Figure 1. If you have this type of PLC, no changes should be necessary. If you are using other PLCs, you can easily change the ladder diagram to suit, or write it into the required mnemonic instructions.

Remember too that the number system for the Toshiba is different from those of many other machines. Again, you should have no difficulty in converting to numbers suitable for the particular PLC you are using.

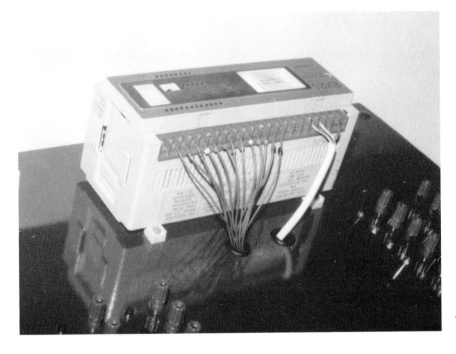

◀ Figure 1 A typical programmable logic controller

PLC system overview

In order to be able to operate and program a PLC you need to know:

- the program format
- the instruction set
- the internal functions available
- the number of inputs/outputs (I/Os) available
- the methods of addressing the above.

You should be able to find this information in the manufacturer's handbook for your PLC.

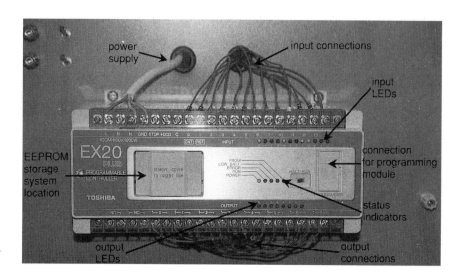

▶ **Figure 1.1** Input and output ports on a typical PLC

Additional information

The program format, in most cases, is a language based on ladder diagrams. This is the language adopted by most of the manufacturers because it is relatively easy to understand when related to logic circuits. Some manufacturers, however, require the ladder diagram to be converted into an abbreviated statement to enable it to be loaded into a PLC or a Boolean logic statement. Whichever method is used, it is generally quite easy to move from one PLC to another with the minimum of new understanding required.

Task 1.1 PLC block diagram

Examine a PLC on a piece of plant or on a simulated plant. Note that each of the sensors/switches being used to generate an input signal is fed to an individual terminal on the input side of the PLC. On the output side, each device that is driven by the PLC is similarly linked to an individual terminal. What other connections are made to the output terminal strip?

From your observations of a PLC, draw a block diagram of the PLC together with the electrical connections made to the I/O devices and power source.

Task 1.2 PLC specification

Using the manufacturer's literature for the PLC, find out and write down the following:

- the number of I/O terminals available and the method of addressing them
- the internal functions available and how they are addressed
- the methods used to include the devices in a ladder diagram.

ADDITIONAL TASK

From the literature, find out:

- the method used by the PLC to 'read' the program
- the amount of memory available for programming.

A POINT TO NOTE

The available memory space of a PLC is limited. When a program is being written, therefore, the programmer should attempt to use all the relevant functions available with a view to minimising the space required.

Logic statements and ladder diagrams

The PLC relies on the processing of binary signals (0 or 1) which form a logical pattern in the central logic relay processor within the PLC.

The processing of these signals can be described best in terms of the three basic logic functions

- AND
- OR
- NOT.

All combinational control problems can be solved using these three basic operations, or a combination of them.

The AND logic operation relates to the output signal Y. This will become 1 only when *all* the inputs are 1. This is written as

$A \wedge B = Y$ or $A . B = Y$

That is, Y is equal to 1 only when A = 1 AND B = 1.

The OR logic operation again relates to the output signal Y, which will become 1 only when one, several or all the inputs are 1:

$A \vee B \vee C = Y$ or $A + B + C = Y$

That is, Y will equal 1 when A = 1 *or* B = 1 *or* C =1 *or* any combination of the three = 1, or all three = 1.

The NOT logic operation also relates to the output signal: in this case, Y will become opposite to the condition of the input signal. For example, Y will become 0 when A is 1, and vice versa:

$\overline{A} = Y$

That is, Y = 1 when A = 0, or Y = 0 when A = 1.

Additional information

The relationship between the input signals and the output signals is used by the PLC to operate plant and machinery. This is done by converting the logic statement into a ladder diagram representing the input and output devices. If the input signals match the logic within the program, then the output device is activated.

Look, for example, at this logic statement:

$A \vee B = Y$ (A OR B = Y)

This can be converted to a ladder diagram, as in Figure 2.1(a).

Because the letters A and B represent the I/O terminal numbers, they should be represented by numbers relating to the terminal numbers on your PLC, as in Figure 2.1(b) (opposite). On the Toshiba EX20/40, inlet terminals are represented by 'X', and outlets by 'Y'.

Figure 2.1(b) shows that if contact X000 OR X001 is closed, then output Y000 will become active.

Input the ladder diagram in Figure 2.1(b) into your PLC, operate the designated inputs and check that the correct output is operated.

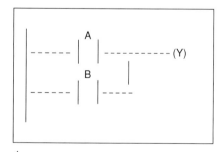

▲ **Figure 2.1(a)**

Task 2.1 Logic statements to ladder diagrams

Convert each of the following logic statements to the equivalent ladder diagram:

A.B.C = Y
A + B.C = Y
A.B + C.D = Y
A.B + C.D = Y

Task 2.2 Lighting circuit

A lamp must operate if any of three switches are operated (Figure 2.2).
Draw up the logic statement for this operation.
Also draw the ladder diagram for loading into a PLC if the switches are connected to input terminals X000, X003 and X005 respectively, and the lamp is operated via output terminal Y008. If necessary, using the number system for your PLC, convert this into the statement language for your machine. Input this into the PLC and check that it operates satisfactorily.

ADDITIONAL TASK

Convert the ladder diagram in Task 2.2 so that the lamp only operates if any two of the three switches, but not the third switch, are operated.

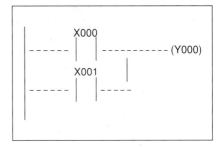

▲ **Figure 2.1(b)**

POINTS TO NOTE

You may need to convert the ladder diagram to a statement language and change the terminal numbers in order to input the program into your particular PLC.

When you are looking at a control problem before developing a ladder diagram, it may be helpful to draw up a simple flow diagram.

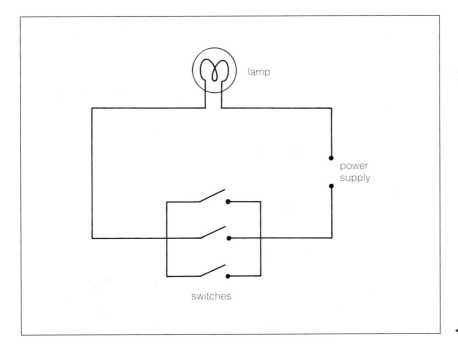

◀**Figure 2.2** Lighting circuit

Learning Assignment 3

Mnemonic listing and truth tables

An instruction set gives the symbols to be used for the development of a PLC program (Figure 3.1).

It is advantageous, however, to develop a formal method of approach in order to ensure that all the requirements of the system are met. One suggested method is set out below.

- Draw up an input and output assignment list. Identify the terminal to which each of the input and output devices is to be connected.
- Draw up a simple truth table of the functions required, using 1s and 0s to identify the relative relationships of the inputs and outputs.

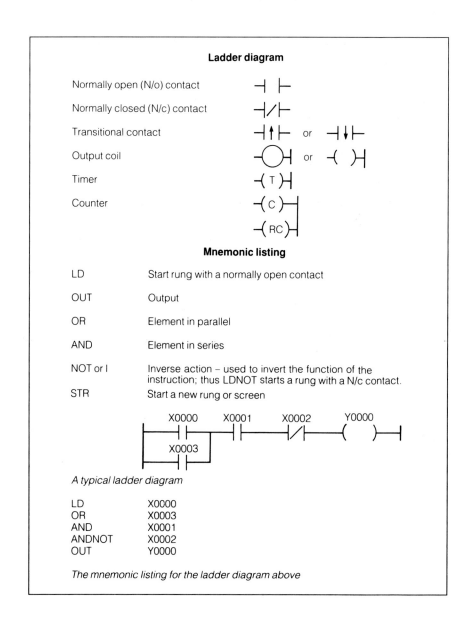

▶ **Figure 3.1** Instruction set examples

- Identify the internal devices required by the system, such as timers, counters and the internal relays required. Identify also any values which may have to be programmed, such as time-out values for timers (5 seconds, for instance).
- Draw up the ladder diagram using the above information.
- If required, convert the ladder diagram to a statement or mnemonic listing.
- Load into the PLC.

Additional information

Using the above method, or a similar one, it will make it easier to identify faults or to trace problems fully, because it simplifies the identification of input/output components and their connections on the PLC. It will also help to locate them on the program.

TASKS

Task 3.1 Circuit truth table

Draw up the input/output assignment list and build a truth table to meet the circuit diagram in Figure 3.2. ('C.R.' represents a control relay.)

Task 3.2 Circuit ladder diagram and mnemonic listing

Draw up the ladder diagram and mnemonic listing to satisfy the control circuit, shown in Figure 3.2. (You may need to refer to the manufacturer's manual for details of how to do this for your particular PLC.)

ADDITIONAL TASK

Develop a Boolean equation and a logic statement to meet the requirements of the control circuit shown in Figure 3.2.

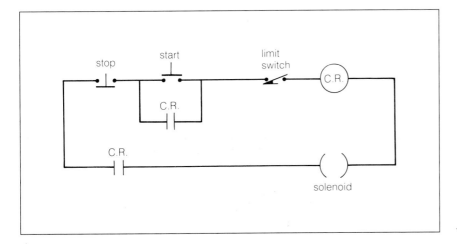

◀ **Figure 3.2** Tasks 3.1 and 3.2

TASKS

Task 3.3 Checkweigh operation

A PLC is used to reject faulty packets of biscuits after a checkweigh operation has been carried out (Figure 3.3).

The packets are transported over a checkweigh machine which ensures that the weights are within set points. Any packet that is outside the limits generates a signal to the PLC. When a faulty packet is detected a pneumatic blower is activated to blow the packet off the conveyor into a reject bin. The blower is stopped as the next packet reaches the checkweigh machine.

Develop, test and run a program on a PLC to simulate this operation.

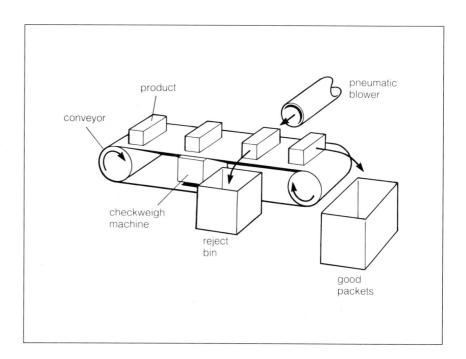

▶ **Figure 3.3** Checkweigh operation

Learning Assignment 4

Internal relays

Included in the instruction set of even the smallest PLC are several basic internal devices. These may be used to enhance the operation of the controlled system and to ease the task of the program writer. The most common of these is the **internal relay** (generally represented by 'R').

This operates in the same way as an ordinary relay (coil), except that it does not directly have an external operation. In order to use the internal coil it has to be activated on a 'rung' and then attached to its output on a separate 'rung'.

TASKS

Task 4.1 Internal coils and external devices

An internal coil can be used to latch on an external device so that when the input signal is lost the output is not de-activated.

Input the ladder diagram shown in Figure 4.1, run the PLC and note the following actions:

- On rung 1, when N/O input X000 is closed, the internal relay R000 and the output Y000 are activated, because R000 has also been designated as N/O input and OR'd round X000 (that is, it provides an alternative to X000). Output Y000 will remain active because R000 is acting as a latch until input X001 is used to de-activate it.
- On rung 2, R000 is used as a N/O contact to drive a separate output (Y001). This operation may be called for anywhere in the program.

An alternative method is to use a **latched coil** ('L'). This device differs from the above in that it remembers its last switched condition on power loss. When the power is returned to the system, the relay will therefore return to the same condition as before.

Task 4.2 Ladder diagram operation

Input the ladder diagram in Figure 4.2 (overleaf). Observe its operation when you switch off the main supply and then return it, and compare it with that of the one in Task 4.1.

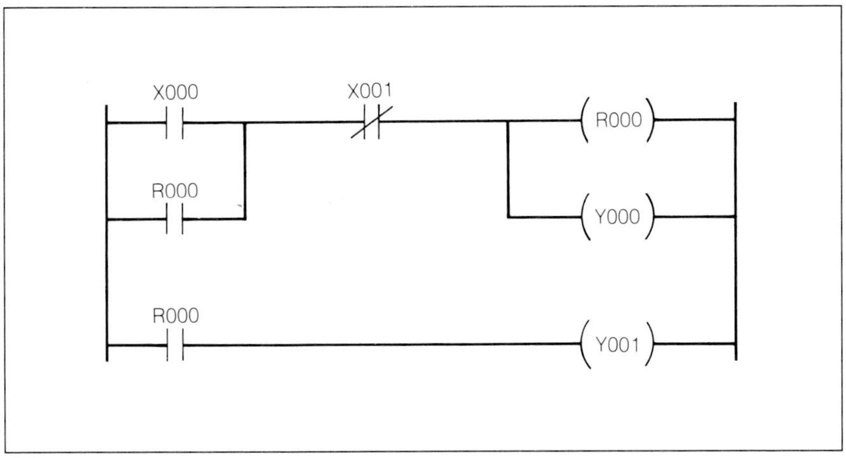

◀ **Figure 4.1** Task 4.1

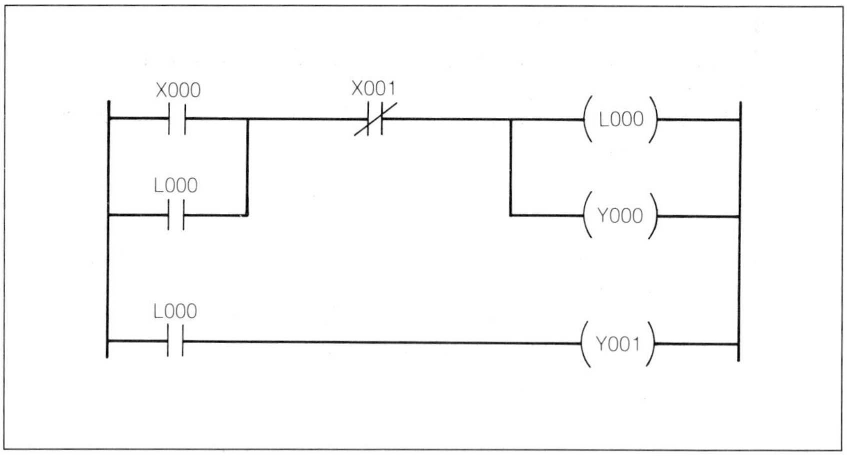

▶ **Figure 4.2** Ladder diagram operation

Additional Information

The latched coil should **not** be used on machinery which is not fully protected. The reason is that when the power is returned to the system it may cause physical action that could result in personal injury.

Remember that, while any external output device may be used to latch itself on, there must always be the facility to unlatch.

TASKS

Task 4.3 Switching program

Input the ladder diagram in Figure 4.3. Then follow the instructions set out below.

- Run the PLC, switch X000 ON and then OFF. Output Y000 will have latched ON. Switch X001 to delatch the output so that Y000 goes OFF. Switch X000 ON and then OFF again. Leave output Y000 ON.
- Switch X002 ON and then OFF, output Y001 latches ON. Check that X003 delatches output Y001. Switch X002 ON and OFF, Y001 should latch ON again.
- Switch the power to the PLC OFF and then ON again. Output Y000 will have delatched, but output Y001 will have come back ON again.

Why is this?

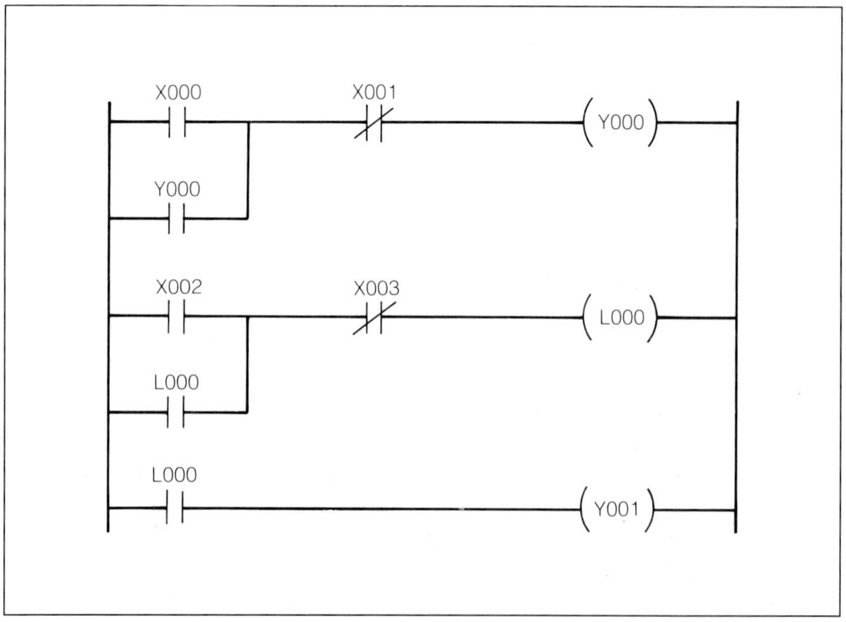

▶ **Figure 4.3** Switching program

12

Task 4.4 Automatic door

A PLC is to be used to control an automatic door into a warehouse (Figure 4.4).

In this example, four input devices are used to develop the control signals to the PLC:

- an ultrasonic device which switches as the vehicle approaches the door
- a photoelectric switch which activates as the vehicle is passing through the doorway
- at the top and bottom positions of the door travel there are limit switches that indicate the position of the door.

When the door is in the down position and the ultrasonic device senses the approach of a vehicle, the PLC will signal the motor drive mechanism to open the door until it reaches the upper limit.

As the vehicle passes through the open door, it breaks the light beam that controls the photoelectric switch. This, along with the upper limit switch signal, reverses the door so closing it until the bottom limit is reached.

Develop, test and run on a PLC a program to simulate the above operation.

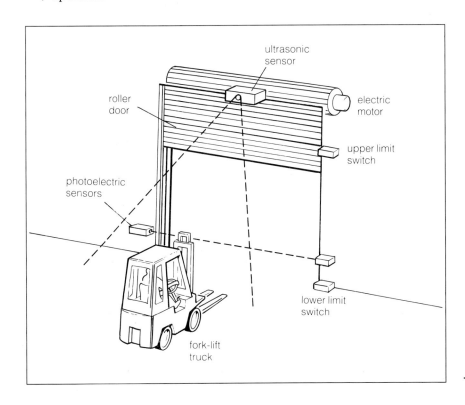

◀ **Figure 4.4** Automatic door operation

ADDITIONAL TASK

Produce a ladder diagram for a machine safety interlock, given that the machine in question has the following features:

- a single-action START button, normally open (X000)
- a single-action STOP button, normally closed (X001)
- a limit switch detecting that the machine's safety guard is closed (X002)
- a light beam in front of the machine; if this beam is broken the machine will stop (X003)
- the starter for the machine's motor is connected to output Y001
- when the guard is in place a spotlight illuminates the work area (Y000).

Learning Assignment 5

Timers

The second most common type of internal device built into PLCs is the **timer** (represented by 'T').

The timer sets a precisely timed interval that must elapse before an operation is activated. It may operate in either OFF–delay–ON or ON–delay–OFF mode.

A timer is normally represented as a coil. When power is supplied to the timer via the input contacts, it times-out and then either opens or closes the related external or internal contacts.

When the power is removed from the timer coil, it will usually reset back to zero in readiness to time-out again. Some larger PLCs, however, have retentive timers that will continue the timing-out on power reset.

A timer is defined by its number, followed by its time-out value. The timers in some PLCs give a choice of pulse period (0.01, 0.1 or 1.0 seconds), but those in many smaller PLCs only have a fixed pulse of 0.1 seconds.

TASKS

Task 5.1 Simple timing circuit

A simple timing circuit program is shown in Figure 5.1. Input this, run the PLC and observe the following actions:

- In rung 1 the timer is being set up to give a timed interval of 5 seconds after X000 has been activated. (*Note:* X000 will need to be held in for the duration of the time-out, otherwise the timer will reset itself; alternatively, it may be latched on by an internal coil.)
- This will give a latched output at Y001 which can be reset by X001 on rung 2.

The above timer is known as a **delay–ON timer**, in that the timed output is switched ON after the timer has timed-out.

Task 5.2 Off – delay circuit

An OFF–delay circuit is shown in Figure 5.2. This will give a delay period starting at the time X000 is released after Y000 has been activated. Y000 will be switched OFF after time-out.

Input this into your PLC and check its operation. Watch for the delay *after* the release of X000, not from when Y000 comes ON.

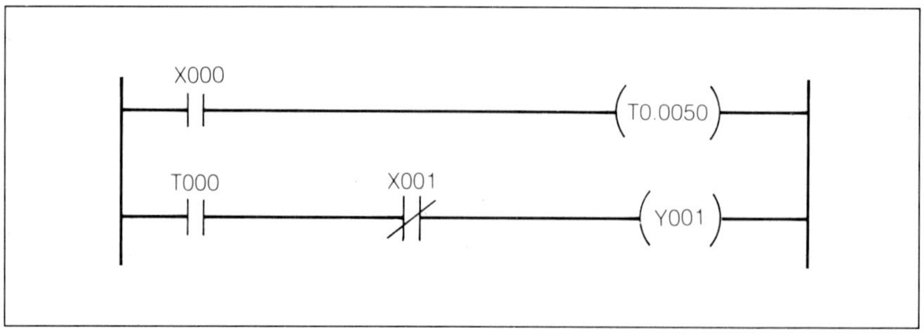

▶ **Figure 5.1** Timing circuit

14

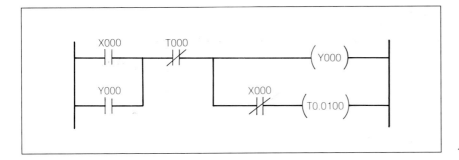

◀ **Figure 5.2** OFF–delay circuit

Additional information

Many of the larger PLCs have individual ON–delay and OFF–delay timers. Individual retentive timers are also available. Modicon PLCs have both ON–delay and OFF–delay timers operated from a single device.

Task 5.3 Machine warning system

A light that pulses ON and OFF at two-second intervals forms part of the warning system on a machine. Develop the part of the program that would operate this sequence continuously until reset externally.

Task 5.4 Segmented conveyor system

A PLC is used to start and stop motors of a segmented conveyor system (Figure 5.3). This permits only those belts actually carrying an object to be moving.

As soon as the power is switched to the PLC, motor 1 starts up and remains running all the time. The plate's arrival opposite sensor 1 elicits a signal from this sensor that operates motor 2. The plate then transfers to belt 2.

When the plate reaches sensor 2, the input signal from this causes the PLC to signal the start of motor 3 and then to stop motor 2 some ten seconds later.

The plate continues on belt 3 until it reaches sensor 3, which signals to the PLC that the plate has reached this point. The PLC must next time-down for five seconds, and then stop motor 3 after the plate has moved on to the next section.

Develop, test and run a program to simulate this operation.

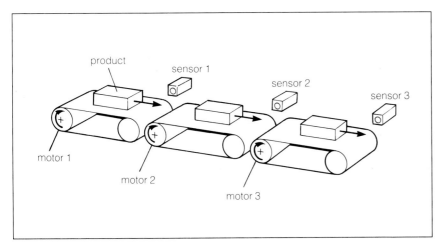

◀ **Figure 5.3** Segmented conveyor system

15

ADDITIONAL TASK

Part of an operating process calls for two items to be bonded together under heat (Figure 5.4):

- after a guard has been lowered by the operator, the items are clamped together by a ram
- five-second delay
- heater operated for ten seconds
- five-second delay
- clamp retracted

Develop a program to operate this part of the sequence using limit switches on the ram to develop the input signals.
    Load your program into the PLC and test.

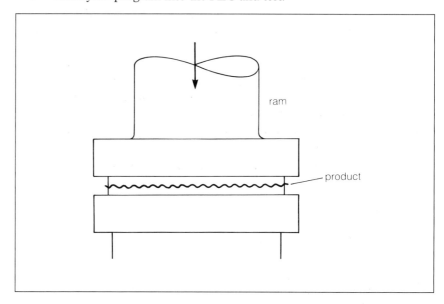

▶ **Figure 5.4** Heat-bonding operation

Counters

The final basic device is a **counter**. A counter (represented by 'C') allows the PLC to generate an output after a predetermined set of actions or events has taken place.

Most counters on small PLCs are 'down' counters, in that they count down from a preset value to zero. When zero is reached, the linked output is activated.

Unlike a timer, a counter requires a reset facility. This resets the preset value ready for the next count. The reset contact can be operated in any one of three different ways:

- By the use of the output signal (Y001). This will hold the reset ON, thus stopping further counts until the output is switched OFF.
- By using the counter itself (C001). This allows counting to restart automatically regardless of the state of the output.
- By the use of a separate external input device (X002). This restarts the count after the external signal.

In Task 6.1 you can edit a program so as to observe each method.

Task 6.1 Reset operations

TASKS

Input the program shown in Figure 6.1 into your PLC and switch to run.

- Operate X001 five times; this will cause Y001 to activate. This will also cause the counter to be reset, but it will not restart counting until the output is reset.
- Edit rung 2 of the program, changing the input to read C001. Run the program again and observe the different reset operation.
- Again edit rung 2, this time changing the reset input to separate input X002, and again observe the change in operation of the counter reset.

A POINT TO NOTE

On the Toshiba, the reset rung needs to be 'live' to enable the counter to count, although this is not so with all models.

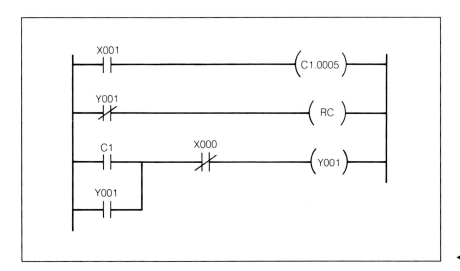

◀ **Figure 6.1** Reset operations

Additional information

As with timers, the same counter should
not be used more than once within a
program.

In many PLCs the timers and counters
use the same internal flags. In that case it
will not be possible to have a timer and a
counter with the same number. For
example, if you have used timer 00,
counter 00 will not be available to you.

If the count is required to go beyond the normal high value of the counter in
use (usually 999), it is possible to cascade several counters together.

TASKS

Task 6.2 Single conveyor system

A single conveyor system is delivering items to two packing stations.
After ten items have been fed to packing station 1 an air cylinder is
operated, driving a gate across the conveyor to direct the next ten to
packing station 2 (Figure 6.2). The system operates continuously as
long as the conveyor is in motion.
   Develop a PLC program to meet these criteria.

ADDITIONAL TASK

As we have said, many counters will not count above 999.
   Develop a program using *only* two counters to count up to 2000, with
neither counter needing to count above 100.

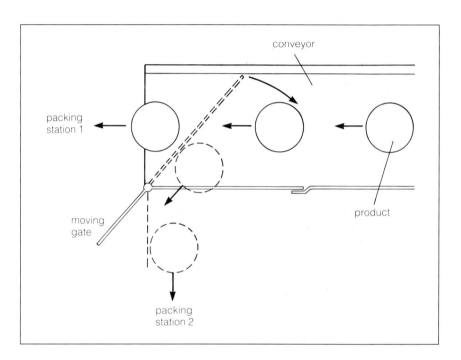

▶ **Figure 6.2** Single conveyor system

Shift registers

A very useful internal instruction available on most PLCs is the **shift register** ('S').

A register is an electronic device in which data is stored. Normally it has 8, 16 or 32 locations (bits), depending on the size of the PLC. With most registers used in PLCs, each individual location within the store is accessible from the program. This is not so with the shift register. Only the first location is available to input values (1 or 0). The shift register then shifts that value from one location to the next in line.

The shift register requires three inputs:

* shift input: used to input a value into the first location
* shift pulse: the signal used by the system to shift the values along by one location
* reset input: used to clear or reset the whole register.

A shift register is often used in a production system where it is necessary to keep track of an individual product item which has been rejected and needs to be removed from the system, away from the point of inspection.

It can also be used to allow a sequence of operations to be followed, ensuring that the previous operation has switched off as the next one comes on.

An example of the first type of operation is shown in Figure 7.1 (overleaf). Input the ladder to your PLC.

Input X000 is the input signal; that is, it generates a 1 or 0 in the first bit of the register.

Input X001 is the shift pulse. Each time this goes high the input signals are shifted one bit to the right.

X002 is the reset. This is used to reset all bits in the register to 0.

In order to input a 1 into the first bit (simulating a faulty item), X000 must be high when X001 is activated, X000 and X001 should then be switched OFF. Next, X001 should be switched ON and then OFF, simulating the items moving down a conveyor system. After three actions output Y001 should activate, giving an output signal to a device that will remove the defective item.

USEFUL OBSERVATIONS

PLCs vary in the operation of the shift register. For example, in the Toshiba method shown in Figure 7.1 the reset rung needs to be live before the shift register will operate.

It is usual to state how many bits in the register are required for use; for example, S000.S007 is using all the bits in a single Toshiba register.

It is possible to cascade several shift registers together if more locations are required than there are bits in the register.

TASKS

Task 7.1 Signals through a shift register

Edit the program in Figure 7.1 using all eight bits connected to eight outputs, so that you can observe the signal travelling through the shift register.

Task 7.2 Pneumatic cylinder system

Pneumatic cylinders are to be operated in a single sequence of A+, A−, B+, B−, C+, C− (Figure 7.2). Each cylinder is driven by a single solenoid-operated valve receiving a signal from a PLC. The input signals to the PLC are generated by a sensor positioned at the end of the inward and outward stroke of each cylinder. To start up the system, two manual buttons must be operated simultaneously.

Develop a PLC program using the shift register to give you this operation.

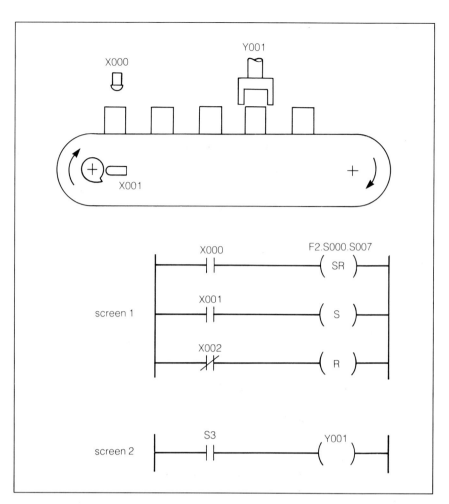

▶ **Figure 7.1** Signals through a shift register

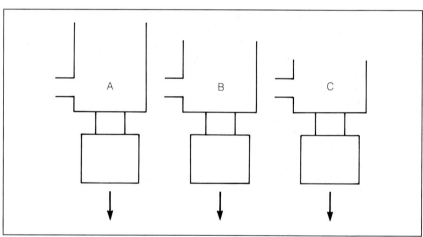

▶ **Figure 7.2** Pneumatic cylinder system

ADDITIONAL TASK

When Task 7.2 is operating correctly, edit the program so as to build in interlocks that will ensure that the output signals match up with the action of the cylinders, thus ensuring correct operation every time.

Task 7.3 Power press machine feed system

A feed belt is used to move blanks into a pressing machine (Figure 7.3). As the blank reaches the jig, limit switch 1 is operated, stopping the belt. This action signals the operation of a pneumatic ram, which pushes the blank into the jig. When the blank is fully home, limit switch 2 is operated. This causes the ram to return to its start position, thus operating limit switch 3. Upon the signal from limit switch 3 a hydraulic ram is operated, pressing the blank through a die; the resulting component is ejected through the base of the die, activating a light

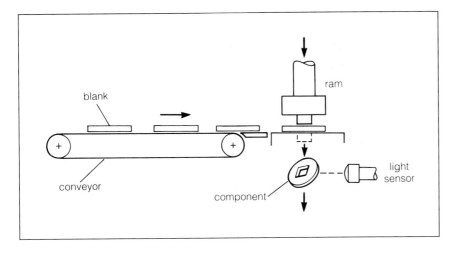

sensor. The signal from this light sensor signals the return of the ram, and the next component can then be moved up to the jig. The process then continues.

Develop a program using a shift register to give this sequence. Load it into the PLC and simulate the operation of the feed system.

Task 7.4 Bottle inspection system

A PLC is used to control an inspection system on a bottle conveyor (Figure 7.4). Each bottle is inspected for the presence of a cap and a label. This is carried out using a capacitive sensor for the cap and a photoelectric sensor for the label.

The conveyor carrying the bottles is operated through a PLC with a start and stop facility.

When a cap or a label is found to be missing, a signal is generated which will stop the conveyor five positions later and then activate the operation of a robot arm which removes the defective bottle and places it on the second conveyor. The main conveyor then restarts, and the second conveyor runs for five seconds to remove the bottle from the immediate area.

The defective bottles placed on to the second conveyor are counted; when the number of bottles reaches a preset value, an audible alarm is sounded intermittently, two seconds on and two seconds off. A warning light is also switched on. These warnings can only be reset by an operator attending the machine and pressing a reset button.

The robot action is programmed separately from the main system.

Develop, test and run a PLC program which will operate the machine in the above sequence.

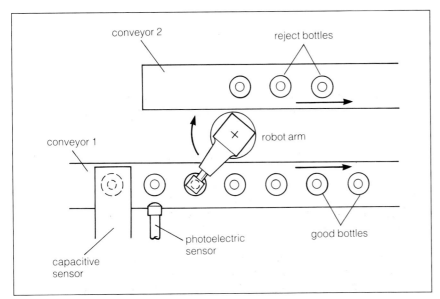

◀ **Figure 7.4** Bottle inspection system

Learning Assignment 8

Master and jump controls

In order to help towards better control of equipment, many PLCs have a **master control coil** and a **jump control coil**.

The master control coil establishes an area within a program which can be controlled by one rung of the ladder diagram. In order to operate this device, the portion of the diagram requiring control is placed between a master control SET rung and a master control RESET rung. During the operation of the program, the PLC will not scan this centre portion unless the SET rung is active. When the SET rung is de-activated, all the operations called for in this intermediate section are immediately isolated from the rest of the program and switched off, irrespective of their condition at the time.

The jump coil also establishes an area within the program which is controlled by the jump coil SET rung, and a RESET rung. But this facility operates in entirely the opposite way to the master control coil, in that all operations in the intermediate rungs work as normal when the SET rung is inactive. Also, when the SET rung is activated all operations stop but retain their status; they then continue their sequences when the SET rung is de-activated.

Additional information

Many programs use the master control coil to operate an emergency stop function, but under present legislation any such system must also be hard-wired.

TASKS

Task 8.1 Master control coil operation

Input the example program of a master control coil operation shown in Figure 8.1. Run the PLC and then operate input X001, observing the change in operation.

Task 8.2 Jump control coil set and reset

Edit the previous program, replacing the master control coil with the jump coil SET and RESET instructions. Download the new program, switch the PLC to run, and observe the new operation when input X001 is activated.

ADDITIONAL TASK

State the difference in operation that would occur if Task 7.2 was placed under the control of the master control coil instead of that of the jump control coil.

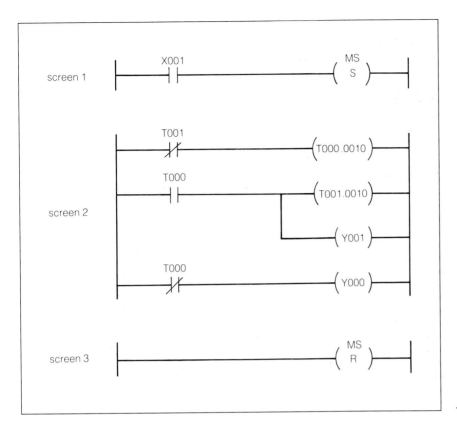

◀ **Figure 8.1** Master control coil operation

System monitoring

All PLCs have the facility to monitor and control various internal and external devices. This allows maintenance personnel to track down faults in the PLC system more easily. It also allows changes to be made to the program, and for it to be checked for correct operation before it is used by the system.

Monitoring involves the condition of devices being 'watched' as they operate during the running of a program. There is normally more than one method available, depending upon the capability of the PLC. The most common is single device monitoring, but rotational monitoring may also be available.

A second facility available under this heading is that of **forcing**. This allows an input or a coil to be set or reset from the program input device (for example, a hand programmer, Figure 9.1), either for a single scan or permanently.

In order to operate the monitoring mode there is normally a key marked MONITOR or MON. This key may be operated when the cursor on the screen has been placed under the symbol for the device by the use of the directional movement arrows, or by using the SEARCH facility on the PLC. When a device is being monitored an indication that it is energised will be given on the screen, either by highlighting or by the filling in of the symbol. It is also possible to observe a timer or counter operating. The information given will normally be that the timer/counter is active, together with the elapsed time or count, and also the activation of a device after a given time or count.

TASKS

Task 9.1 Master control coil monitoring

Input the program from Task 8.2 and ensure its correct operation. Using the monitor facility available on your PLC, monitor the operation of the master control coil, timer 000 and the output Y000.

ADDITIONAL TASK

Edit the program in Task 9.1 to increase the timer values to 30 seconds. Download it to the PLC, and monitor the timers to ensure correct operation.

Additional information

When the 'force' facility has been used to 'force' a device into a condition, remember that the device remains in that condition regardless of the requirement of the program. Therefore the 'force' condition must *always* be cancelled before the PLC is returned to normal operation.

TASKS

Task 9.2 Using search facilities

- Input the program shown in Figure 9.2, and run it to ensure correct operation. Using the correct method for your PLC, 'force' input X000 to the OPEN condition.
- Activate input X001. If you now monitor the rung, you should find that this signal is ignored, because X000 is locked into the OPEN condition. This prevents the completion of the rung to activate output Y000.
- Reset the input to normal.
- Using the SEARCH facility, locate coil Y002 and 'force' this into the OFF condition. Activate input X001. What is the result of this operation?
- Reset all conditions to normal.

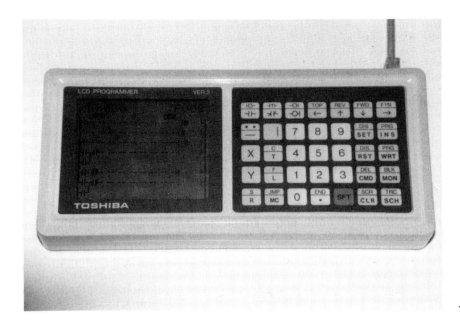

◀ **Figure 9.1** A typical hand programmer

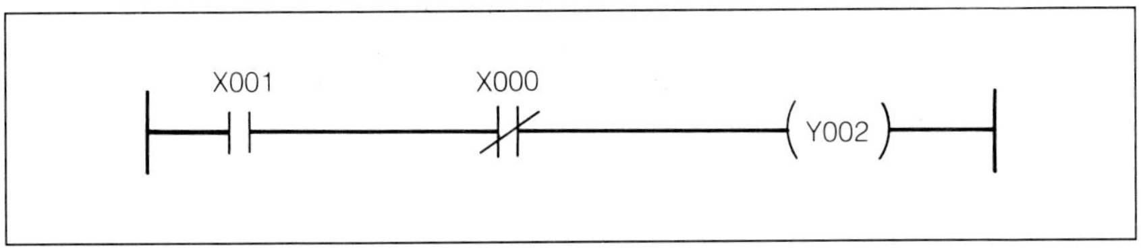

◀ **Figure 9.2** Task 9.2

Projects

So far in this book the assignments and tasks have been designed to help you develop the skills you need to program and use the various devices available on a PLC. The projects that follow aim to bring all these elements together into programs that represent real problems which have actually been solved in industry by the use of a PLC.

For each of the following projects, develop a program on an available PLC. Load and test by simulation and then correct if necessary, so that a fully operating program is achieved.

Each project has been designed to allow you to develop the program in its basic form without any difficulty. Your lecturer or supervisor can add several degrees of difficulty to each project, to extend your skills still further.

Project 1 Mixing system

A PLC is used to control the mixing of the ingredients for biscuit manufacture. The ingredients are first mixed in two vessels, one for dry ingredients and one for wet (Figure P1), the required ingredients being weighed and fed into the mixers by hand.

- The 'dry' mixer churns the ingredients by the use of a paddle, which is rotated by an electric motor for five minutes. In the 'wet' mixer the ingredients are heated to a predetermined temperature and then mixed by a pump unit circulating them for five minutes.
- When each tank has followed the required mixing routine, slide valves are operated pneumatically and the ingredients are fed by gravity into the main mixing tank to be mixed together. This tank is fitted with a motorised paddle, a heater to maintain the temperature and a load cell to ensure proper batch size.
- After mixing for ten minutes the mixture is fed into one of three holding vessels under gravity to await forming and baking. This section is then controlled by a further PLC.

Project 2 Baking system

After the biscuits have been formed they are fed on to a conveyor system for baking. The oven (gas-fired), the conveyor, the inspection and partial packing are controlled by a PLC as follows (Figure P2).

- The START button is pressed to commence the sequence of operations. This activates the ignition spark and opens the pilot gas valve. A flame sensor detects the pilot flame; if there is no flame within five seconds the pilot valve is closed. Otherwise the valve remains open and the ignition spark is turned off.
- The main gas valve then opens and, provided the thermostat indicates a low temperature and the pilot flame is lit, the burners ignite.
- When the required temperature is reached in the oven the main gas burners are turned off, leaving only the pilot flame burning. When the temperature falls to the set point, a delay of five seconds is followed by ignition of the main gas burners by the pilot flame. Should any flame fail at any time, both the main gas and the pilot valves are shut instantly and remain closed until the start-up procedure is repeated.
- When the oven is at the correct temperature the conveyor will start and pass the biscuits through the oven to be baked. When the biscuits have been baked they are checked for correct colour by a sensor, with any

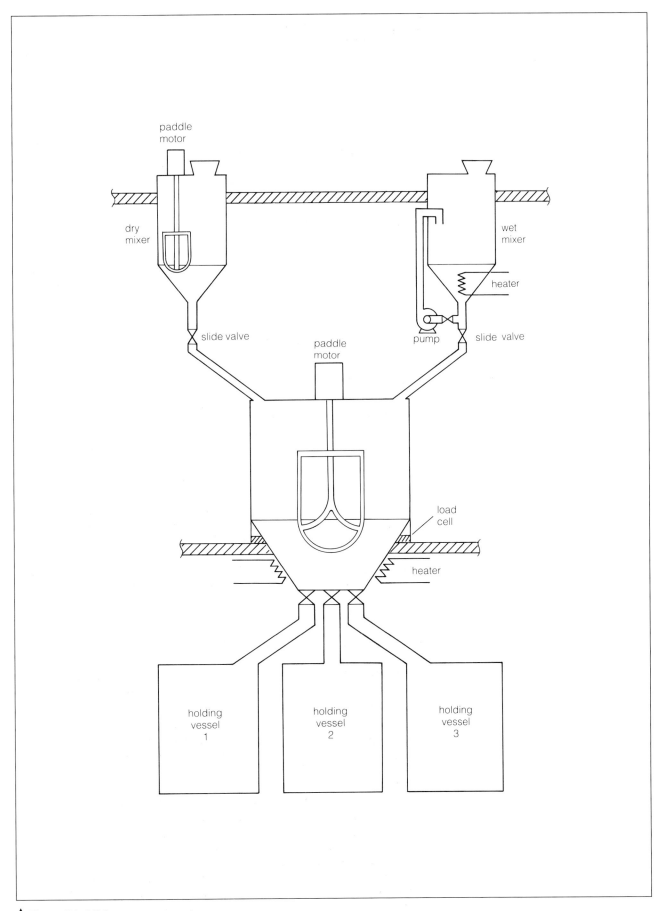

▲ **Figure P1** Mixing system

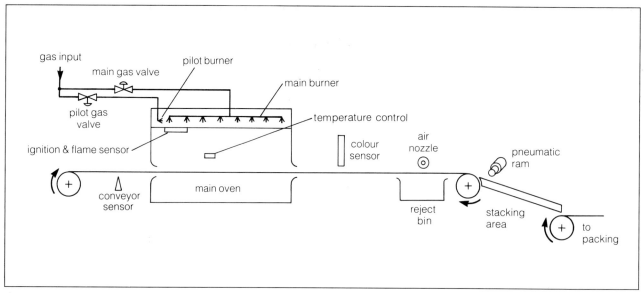

▲ **Figure P2** Conveyor/oven system

defective biscuit being removed from the conveyor some ten positions
down the line by an air blast that blows it into a reject hopper.

● After baking and inspection the biscuits are fed into the stacking area prior
to packing. The stacker counts the biscuits and directs twenty biscuits into
one of four lanes by the use of a pneumatically controlled arm so that they
can then be wrapped and packed.

The next operation is then controlled by a further PLC.

Project 3 Packing system

After the biscuits have been wrapped they are loaded on to a conveyor in the
vertical position, which allows them to be packed into cartons under the
control of a PLC (Figures P3 and P4).

● The packets move along the conveyor towards collection points beneath
an identical pair of pick and place units. Alongside each unit is a second
conveyor which carries empty boxes that stop when in position beneath
the pick and place units.

● When the first collection point is full, a pneumatic ram is operated to
divert the packets into the second collection point.

● Meanwhile, the first pick and place unit picks up six packets by means of
suction cups, transfers them to a position over a box, lowers them into the
box and then releases the vacuum.

● The picking arm then returns to its home position and the full box is
replaced by a new one.

The two pick and place units work in exactly the same way, each in turn
placing six packets in a box.

This sequence is repeated continuously as long as there are packets on the
conveyor.

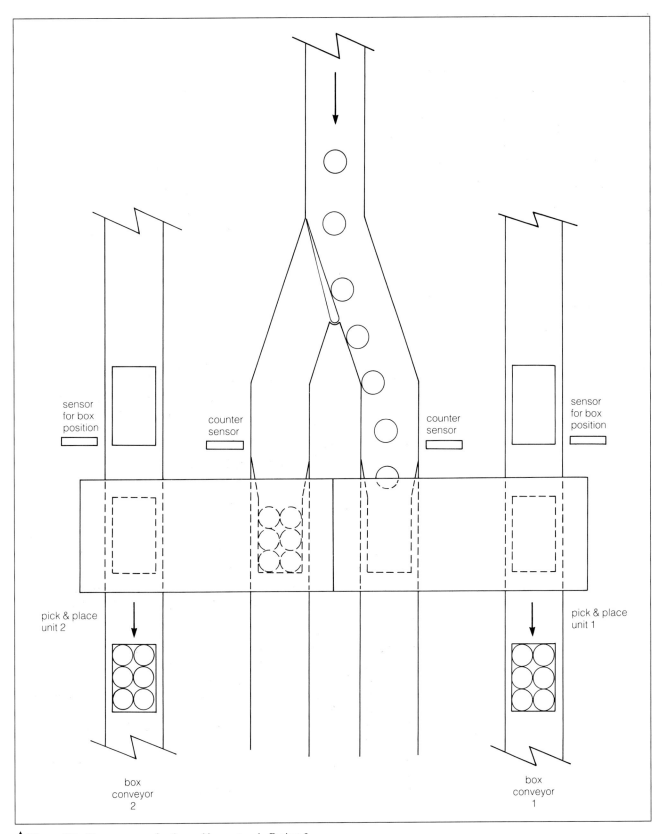

▲ **Figure P3** The conveyors for the packing system in Project 3

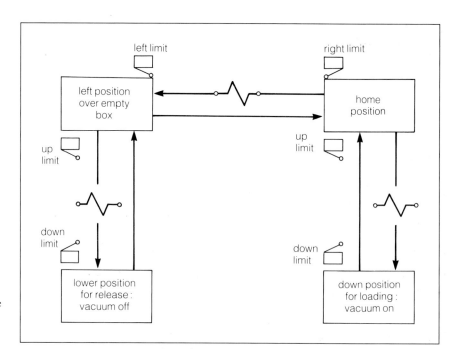

▶ **Figure P4** Relative positions for pick
and place unit (the second unit will be the
mirror image of the one shown); the
pneumatic cylinders are controlled by
single-solenoid spring-return DCVs

Glossary

Address   Internal location of a bit

Binary signal   An ON or OFF signal
Bit   A binary digit of data
Boolean equation   Method used to determine the overall logic function

Download   Transfer of program from writing device to PLC

EEPROM   Electronically Erasable Programmable Read Only Memory
EPROM   Electronically Programmable Read Only Memory

Flag   Internally available device, such as a timer or relay
Flow diagram   Outline of the sequence of events
Forcing   Operating an external device via the programming keyboard

Instruction set   Detail of the availability of functions within the PLC
I/O   Inputs and outputs on the PLC

Jump   To move to another part of the program via software

Ladder diagram   Method of writing program instructions
Latch   To lock on a signal
Load   Transfer a program (for example, from PLC to EPROM)
Logic diagram   Symbolic diagram indicating logic functions required

Memory   Program storage device
Mnemonic listing   High-level 'shorthand' instruction to the PLC
Mode   The operation that the PLC is switched to

N/C   Normally closed
N/O   Normally open

Program   The complete set of instructions to the PLC

Register   Defined number of bits
Rung   Unit part of the ladder diagram

Scan   Method of reading a program
Sensor   Device used to generate an input signal
Software   Internal operating program
Statement language   High-level programming method

Truth table   Digitial outline of logic operation

VDU   Visual display unit

Index